STANDARD OF EXCELLENCE

ENHANCED COMPREHENSIVE BAND METHOD

By Bruce Pearson

Dear Student:

Welcome to the wonderful world of instrumental music. The moment you pick up your French horn, you will begin an exciting adventure that is filled with challenges and rewards. If you study carefully and practice regularly, you will quickly discover the joy and satisfaction of playing beautiful music for yourself, your family, your friends, or a concert audience.

I hope you have many rewarding years of music-making.

Best wishes,

Bruce Pearson

Practice and Assessment - the key to EXCELLENCE!

▶ Make practicing part of your daily schedule. If you plan it as you do any other activity, you will find plenty of time for it.

▶ Try to practice in the same place every day. Choose a place where you can concentrate on making music. Start with a regular and familiar warm-up routine, including long tones and simple technical exercises. Like an athlete, you need to warm-up your mind and muscles before you begin performing.

▶ Always tune before you play. Use the tuning tracks found on the Accompaniment Recordings, or use the *iPAS* Tuner.

▶ Set goals for every practice session. Keep track of your practice time and progress on the front cover Practice Journal.

▶ Practice the difficult spots in your lesson assignment and band music over and over at a slower tempo, until you can play them perfectly, then gradually increase the tempo. Use the *iPAS* Metronome to track your progress and ensure you are playing with a steady pulse.

▶ Spend time practicing alone and with the Accompaniment Recordings.

▶ Assess your progress and achievements by using *iPAS*. Listen to the recordings you create to hear the spots in the music which might need improvement.

▶ In cases where there is more than one version of an exercise (see 29. GO FOR EXCELLENCE!), *iPAS* always assesses the first one.

▶ When notes appear in octaves (see 31. TRIED AND TRUE), *iPAS* assesses the upper note.

▶ In the *iPAS* fingering charts, select Tab 1 to show F Horn fingerings. Select Tab 2 for B♭ Horn fingerings.

▶ At the end of each practice session, play something fun!

ISBN 0-8497-0760-9

© 1993, 2004 Neil A. Kjos Music Company, 4382 Jutland Drive, San Diego, California.
International copyright secured. All rights reserved. Printed in U.S.A.

KJOS NEIL A. KJOS MUSIC COMPANY, PUBLISHER

PUTTING YOUR FRENCH HORN TOGETHER

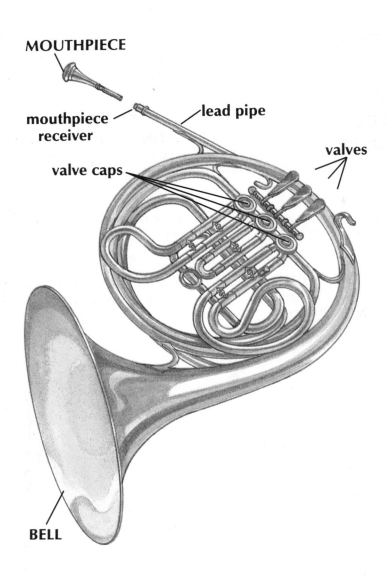

MOUTHPIECE

mouthpiece
receiver

lead pipe

valves

valve caps

BELL

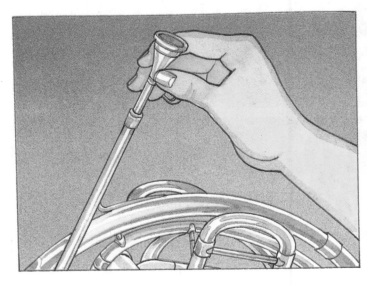

STEP 1
Open your case right side up.

STEP 2
Hold the horn in your left hand. Hold the mouthpiece in your right hand, and place it into the mouthpiece receiver on the lead pipe.

STEP 3
Gently turn the mouthpiece to the right, not too tightly.

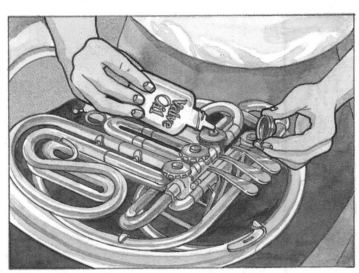

STEP 4
Unscrew the valve caps and add a drop or two of oil if necessary. Replace the valve caps. Work the keys up and down to distribute the oil.

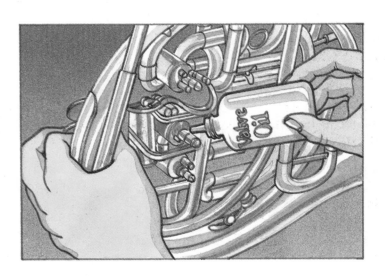

STEP 5
Turn your horn over and put a drop or two of oil in the underside of the valve, into the seam where the axle and its bearing meet. Work the keys up and down to distribute the oil.

PREPARING TO PLAY

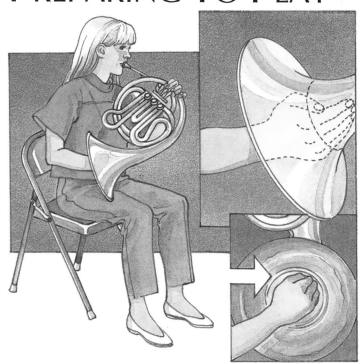

STEP 1
Sit up straight on the edge of your chair.

STEP 2
Rest the bell on your right leg. The actual place will be determined by your height. Do not block the bell with your body.

STEP 3
Cup your right hand with fingers and thumb tightly closed. Put your hand in the bell so only your fingers and thumb touch the side of the bell away from your body.

STEP 4
Place your left little finger in the hook and your left thumb in the ring or on the B♭ thumb valve.

STEP 5
Place the first three fingers of your left hand on the valves. Relax your left arm. Your elbows should be away from your body.

PLAYING YOUR FRENCH HORN

STEP 1
Shape the inside of your mouth as if saying "oh." Bring your lips together as if saying "em."

STEP 2
Your lips should have firm corners but a relaxed center. Your chin should be flat and pointed.

STEP 3
Take a full breath of air and blow, creating a relaxed, buzzing tone.

STEP 4
While buzzing, place the mouthpiece over the buzz with 2/3 of the mouthpiece on the upper lip and 1/3 on the lower lip.

STEP 5
Put the mouthpiece into the lead pipe. Take a full breath of air and play a long, steady tone.

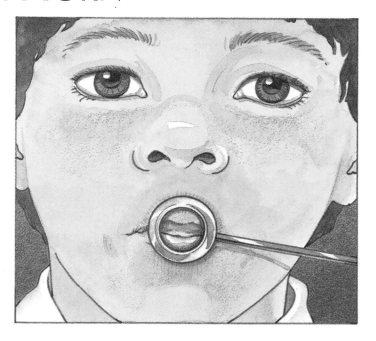

CARING FOR YOUR FRENCH HORN

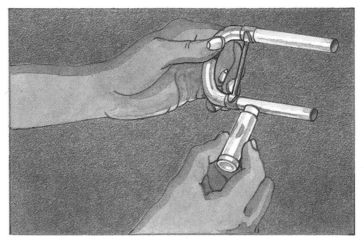

STEP 1
After playing, drain the excess water from your horn. Wipe off your instrument with a soft, clean cloth.

STEP 2
Remove the mouthpiece and put it and your horn carefully in the case and latch it.

STEP 3
Grease your slides regularly.

FOR FRENCH HORNS ONLY

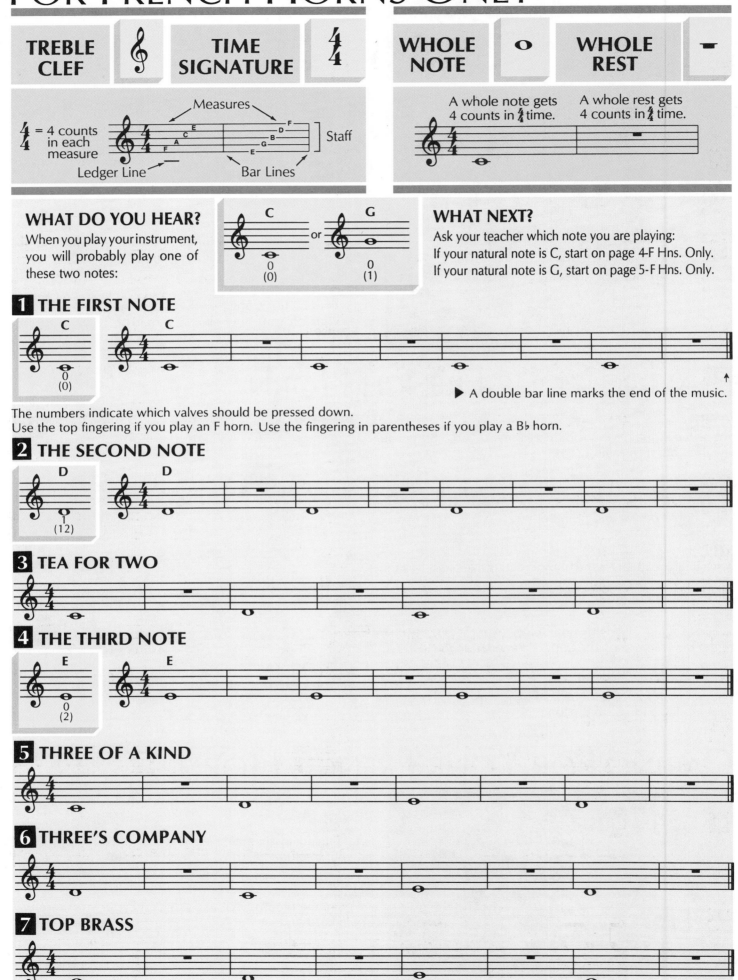

TREBLE CLEF   𝄞   **TIME SIGNATURE**   𝄴   **WHOLE NOTE**   𝅝   **WHOLE REST**   𝄻

4/4 = 4 counts in each measure

Measures — Staff — Ledger Line — Bar Lines

A whole note gets 4 counts in 4/4 time.

A whole rest gets 4 counts in 4/4 time.

WHAT DO YOU HEAR?

When you play your instrument, you will probably play one of these two notes:

C (0)   or   G (1)

WHAT NEXT?

Ask your teacher which note you are playing:

If your natural note is C, start on page 4-F Hns. Only.

If your natural note is G, start on page 5-F Hns. Only.

1 THE FIRST NOTE

C 0 (0)

▶ A double bar line marks the end of the music.

The numbers indicate which valves should be pressed down.
Use the top fingering if you play an F horn. Use the fingering in parentheses if you play a B♭ horn.

2 THE SECOND NOTE

D 1 (12)

3 TEA FOR TWO

4 THE THIRD NOTE

E 0 (2)

5 THREE OF A KIND

6 THREE'S COMPANY

7 TOP BRASS

PW21HF

FOR FRENCH HORNS ONLY

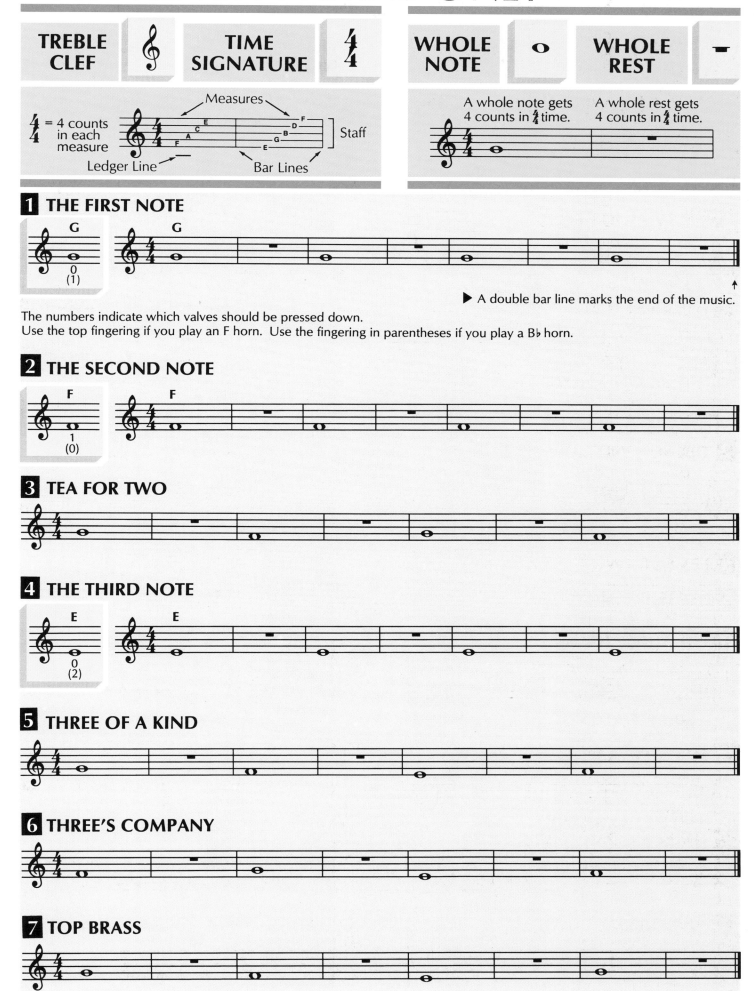

▶ A double bar line marks the end of the music.

The numbers indicate which valves should be pressed down.
Use the top fingering if you play an F horn. Use the fingering in parentheses if you play a B♭ horn.

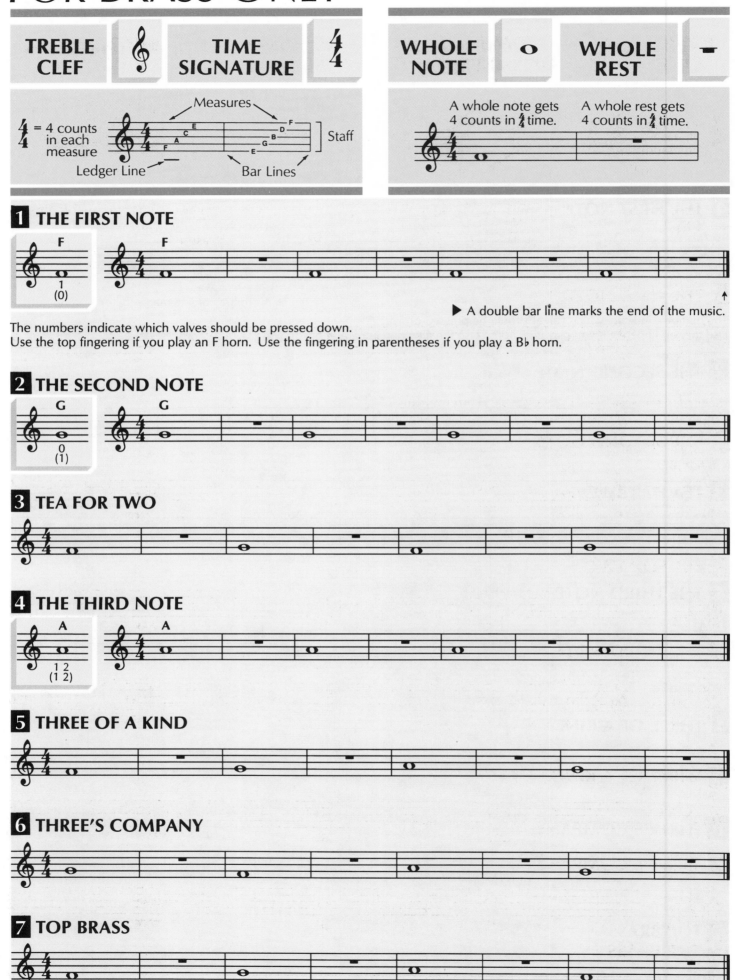

FOR BRASS ONLY

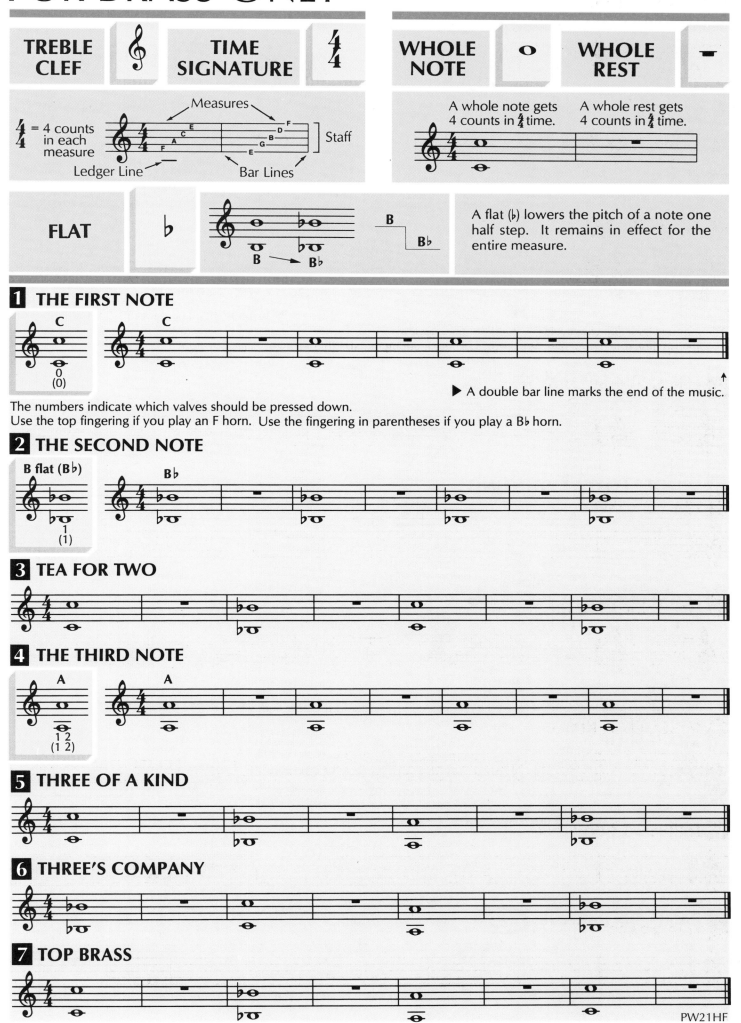

| TREBLE CLEF | 𝄞 | TIME SIGNATURE | 4/4 |

4/4 = 4 counts in each measure

Measures
Staff
Ledger Line
Bar Lines

| WHOLE NOTE | o | WHOLE REST | ▬ |

A whole note gets 4 counts in 4/4 time.
A whole rest gets 4 counts in 4/4 time.

| FLAT | ♭ |

B → B♭

A flat (♭) lowers the pitch of a note one half step. It remains in effect for the entire measure.

1 THE FIRST NOTE

C
0
(0)

► A double bar line marks the end of the music.

The numbers indicate which valves should be pressed down.
Use the top fingering if you play an F horn. Use the fingering in parentheses if you play a B♭ horn.

2 THE SECOND NOTE

B flat (B♭)
1
(1)

3 TEA FOR TWO

4 THE THIRD NOTE

A
1 2
(1 2)

5 THREE OF A KIND

6 THREE'S COMPANY

7 TOP BRASS

PW21HF

FOR THE FULL BAND

| TREBLE CLEF | 𝄞 | TIME SIGNATURE | 4/4 | WHOLE NOTE | o | WHOLE REST | ▬ |

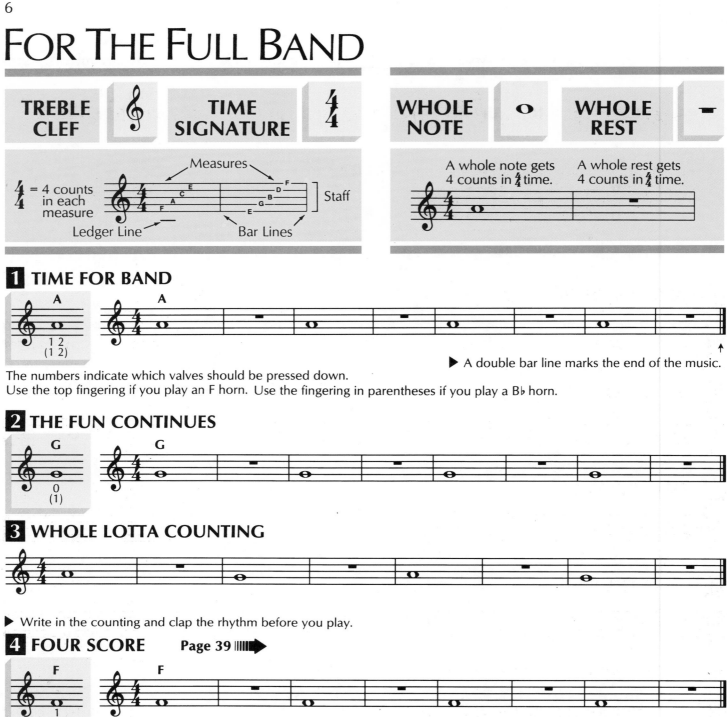

1 TIME FOR BAND

The numbers indicate which valves should be pressed down.
Use the top fingering if you play an F horn. Use the fingering in parentheses if you play a B♭ horn.

▶ A double bar line marks the end of the music.

2 THE FUN CONTINUES

3 WHOLE LOTTA COUNTING

▶ Write in the counting and clap the rhythm before you play.

4 FOUR SCORE Page 39 ▐▐▐▶

▶ When you see a page number followed by an arrow, *Excellerate* to the page indicated for additional studies.

5 MIX 'EM UP

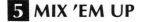

6 MELTING POT

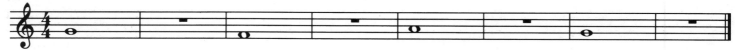

7 BAND ON PARADE

▶ Lines with a medal are *Achievement Lines*. The chart on page 47 can be used to record your progress.

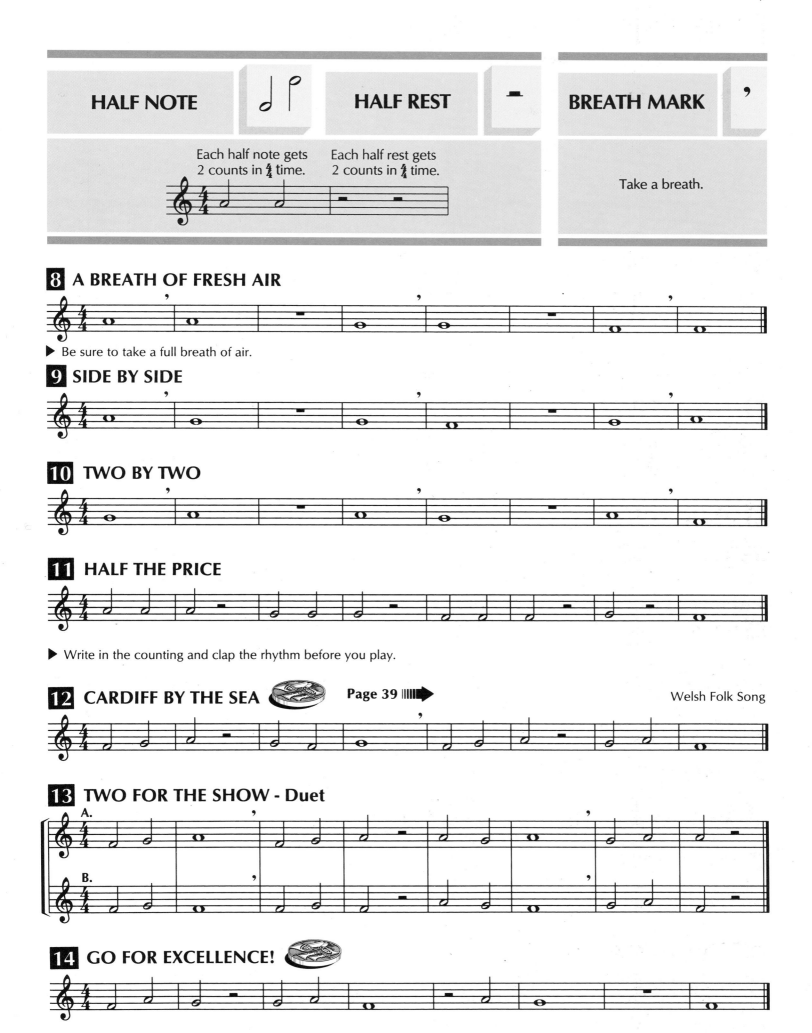

HALF NOTE

HALF REST

BREATH MARK

Each half note gets 2 counts in 4/4 time.

Each half rest gets 2 counts in 4/4 time.

Take a breath.

8 A BREATH OF FRESH AIR

▶ Be sure to take a full breath of air.

9 SIDE BY SIDE

10 TWO BY TWO

11 HALF THE PRICE

▶ Write in the counting and clap the rhythm before you play.

12 CARDIFF BY THE SEA   Page 39 ▷   Welsh Folk Song

13 TWO FOR THE SHOW - Duet

A.

B.

14 GO FOR EXCELLENCE!

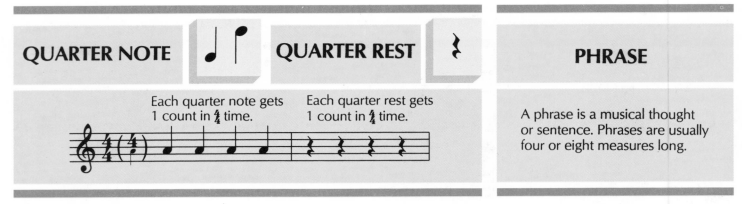

QUARTER NOTE ♩ ♩	QUARTER REST 𝄽	PHRASE
Each quarter note gets 1 count in 𝄴 time.	Each quarter rest gets 1 count in 𝄴 time.	A phrase is a musical thought or sentence. Phrases are usually four or eight measures long.

15 A QUARTER'S WORTH

▶ Write in the counting and clap the rhythm before you play.

16 HOT CROSS BUNS   English Folk Song

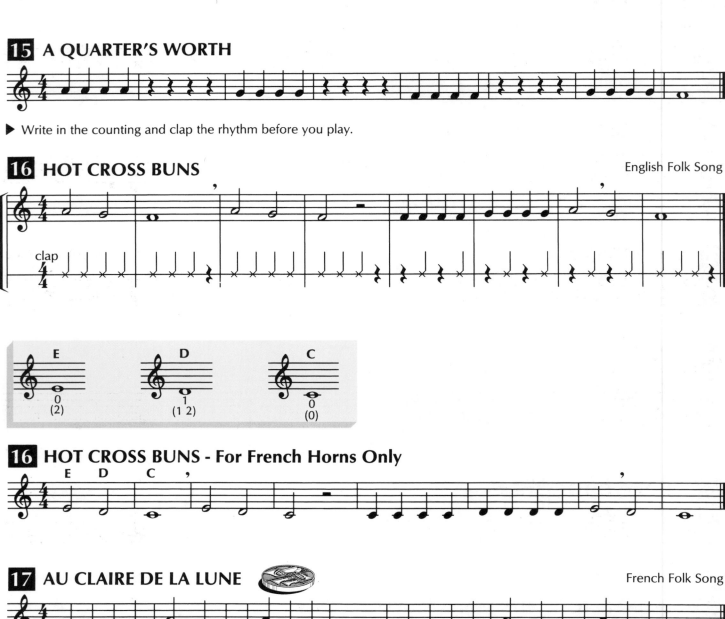

16 HOT CROSS BUNS - For French Horns Only

17 AU CLAIRE DE LA LUNE   French Folk Song

▶ Draw in a breath mark at the end of each phrase.

18 DOWN BY THE STATION   Traditional

FLAT ♭

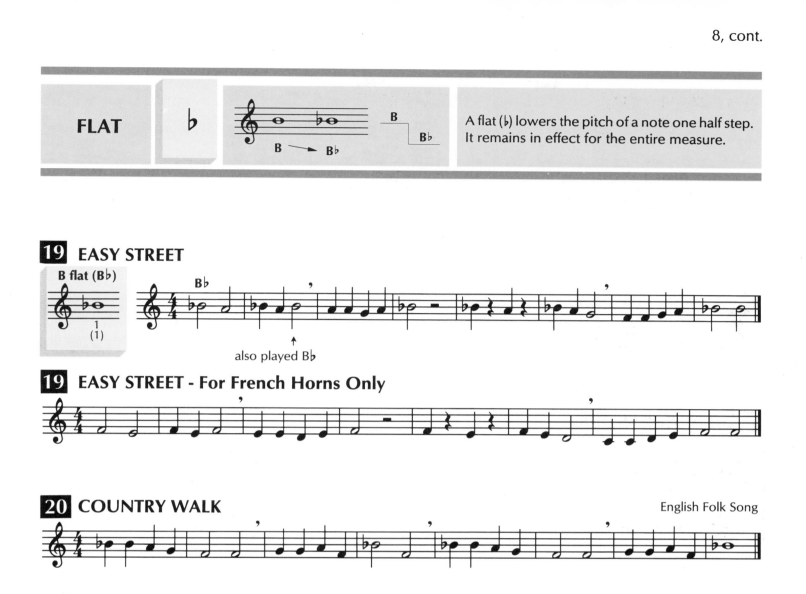

A flat (♭) lowers the pitch of a note one half step. It remains in effect for the entire measure.

19 EASY STREET

B flat (B♭)

also played B♭

19 EASY STREET - For French Horns Only

20 COUNTRY WALK

English Folk Song

20 COUNTRY WALK - For French Horns Only

21 GETTIN' IT TOGETHER

21 GETTIN' IT TOGETHER - For French Horns Only

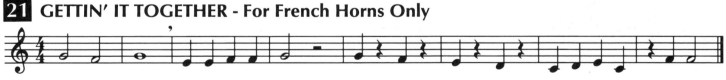

22 FOR FRENCH HORNS ONLY

9

REPEAT SIGN	COMMON TIME	FERMATA
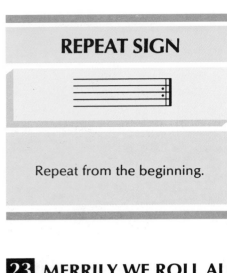	**C**	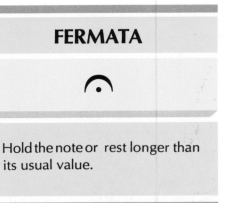
Repeat from the beginning.	**C** = **4/4** Common time means the same as **4/4** time.	Hold the note or rest longer than its usual value.

23 MERRILY WE ROLL ALONG Page 39 ▶▶▶   Traditional

▶ Write in the note names before you play.

23 MERRILY WE ROLL ALONG - For French Horns Only Page 39 ▶▶▶

24 LIGHTLY ROW - Duet   Traditional

25 ONE STEP AT A TIME

▶ Write in the counting and clap the rhythm before you play.

25 ONE STEP AT A TIME - For French Horns Only

SOLO	**SOLI**	**TUTTI**
One person plays.	Whole section plays.	Everyone plays.

26 **GOOD KING WENCESLAS**
Traditional English Carol

Solo/Soli   Tutti   Solo/Soli   Tutti

26 **GOOD KING WENCESLAS - For French Horns Only**

27 **SONG OF THE FJORDS**
Norwegian Folk Song

Solo/Soli   Tutti   Solo/Soli   Tutti

28 _____ Composer _____
your name

▶ Fill in the rest of the measures using the given rhythms and any notes you know. Title and play your composition.

29 **GO FOR EXCELLENCE!**

29 **GO FOR EXCELLENCE! - For French Horns Only**

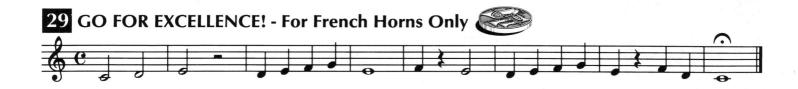

TIE

A tie is a curved line that connects two notes of the <u>same</u> pitch. Tied notes are played as one unbroken note.

30 WARM-UP

▶ Play both octaves on your French horn. Then, try playing this warm-up on your mouthpiece.

30 WARM-UP - For French Horns Only

31 TIED AND TRUE

31 TIED AND TRUE - For French Horns Only

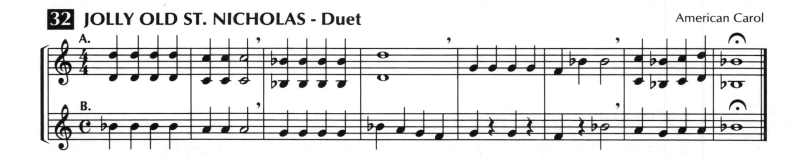

32 JOLLY OLD ST. NICHOLAS - Duet

American Carol

32 JOLLY OLD ST. NICHOLAS - Duet - For French Horns Only

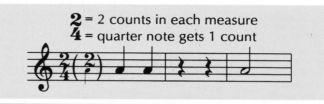

TIME SIGNATURE

33 AMIGOS

Mexican Folk Song

▶ Keep on playing!

▶ Write in the counting and clap the rhythm before you play.

33 AMIGOS - For French Horns Only

34 FARM OUT

Traditional

34 FARM OUT - For French Horns Only

35 FOR FRENCH HORNS ONLY

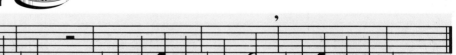

PW21HF

KEY SIGNATURES

Key signatures change certain notes throughout a piece of music. This is the key signature you've been playing so far.

This key signature means play all B's as B flats.

36 MARK TIME

36 MARK TIME - For French Horns Only

37 SWEETLY SINGS THE DONKEY - Round   Traditional

38 MARY ANN   West Indies Folk Song

Solo/Soli   Tutti

Solo/Soli   Tutti

▶ Write in the note names before you play.

38 MARY ANN - For French Horns Only

39 **CRUSADER'S MARCH**  Page 39 ▮▮▮➤ Traditional

▶ Write in the counting and clap the rhythm before you play.

39 **CRUSADER'S MARCH - For French Horns Only** Page 39 ▮▮▮➤

40 **BALANCE THE SCALES**

Draw *one* note or *one* rest to balance each scale.

41 **GO FOR EXCELLENCE!**

41 **GO FOR EXCELLENCE! - For French Horns Only**

BALANCE BUILDER

JINGLE BELLS

Band Arrangement

J. S. Pierpont (1822 - 1893)
arr. Chuck Elledge (b. 1961)

42 SCHOOL SONG

42 SCHOOL SONG - For French Horns Only

43 FOR FRENCH HORNS ONLY

EIGHTH NOTES

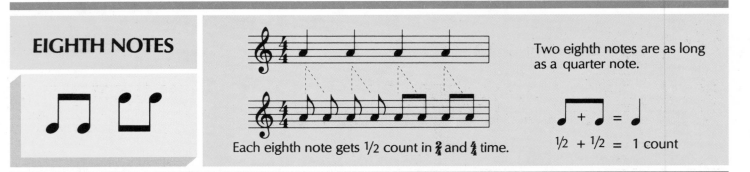

Two eighth notes are as long as a quarter note.

Each eighth note gets ½ count in ⅔ and 4/4 time.

½ + ½ = 1 count

44 WARM-UP

44 WARM-UP - For French Horns Only

45 EIGHTH NOTE ENCOUNTER

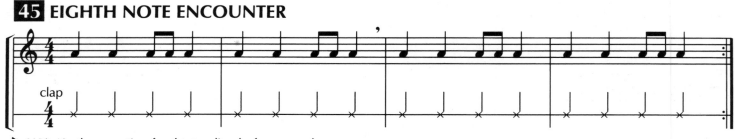

▶ Write in the counting for the top line before you play.

46 JIM ALONG JOSIE

American Folk Song

46 JIM ALONG JOSIE - For French Horns Only

47 EIGHTH NOTE EXPLORER

▶ Write in the counting for the top line before you play.

48 GO TELL BILL

Gioacchino Rossini (1792 - 1868)

48 GO TELL BILL - For French Horns Only

49 GO FOR EXCELLENCE!

49 GO FOR EXCELLENCE! - For French Horns Only

PW21HF

14

50 EIGHTH NOTE EXPRESS

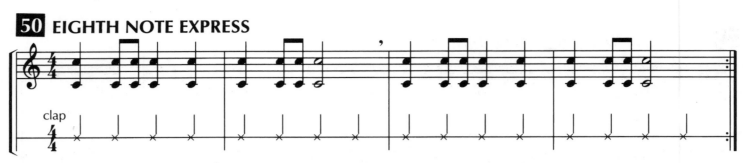

▶ Write in the counting for the top line before you play.

51 SKIP IT, LOU

American Folk Song

52 EIGHTH NOTE EXPERT

▶ Write in the counting for the top line before you play.

53 MEXICAN MOUNTAIN SONG

Mexican Folk Song

53 MEXICAN MOUNTAIN SONG - For French Horns Only

54 BAFFLING BAR LINES

▶ Write in the counting and draw in the bar lines before you play.

54 BAFFLING BAR LINES - For French Horns Only

▶ Write in the counting and draw in the bar lines before you play.

55 FOR FRENCH HORNS ONLY

Theme from "Symphony No. 1"

Gustav Mahler (1860 - 1911)

SLUR	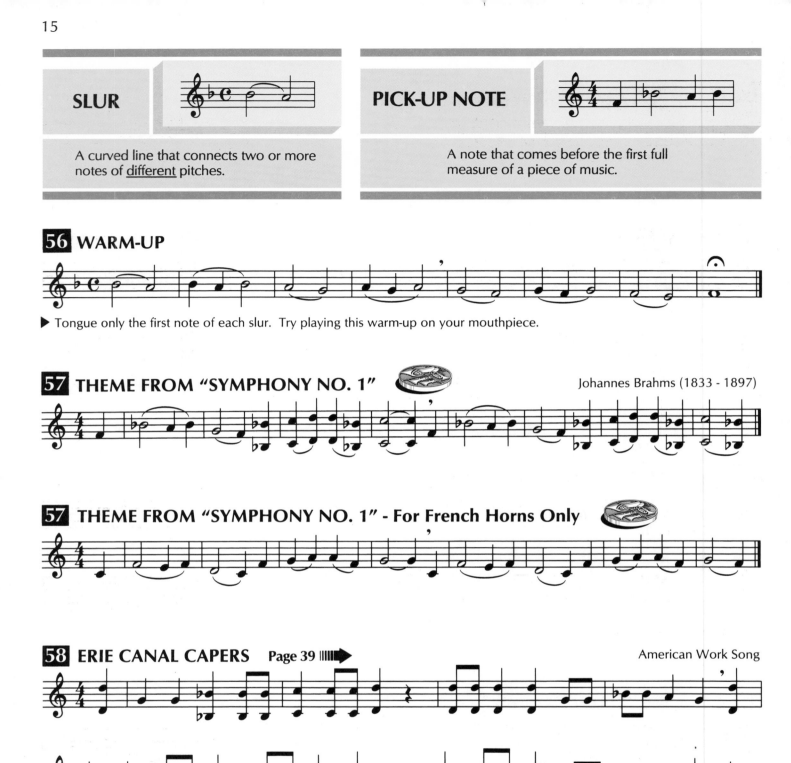

A curved line that connects two or more notes of <u>different</u> pitches.

PICK-UP NOTE

A note that comes before the first full measure of a piece of music.

56 WARM-UP

▶ Tongue only the first note of each slur. Try playing this warm-up on your mouthpiece.

57 THEME FROM "SYMPHONY NO. 1"

Johannes Brahms (1833 - 1897)

57 THEME FROM "SYMPHONY NO. 1" - For French Horns Only

58 ERIE CANAL CAPERS Page 39 ▦➡

American Work Song

58 ERIE CANAL CAPERS - For French Horns Only Page 39 ▦➡

59 LAUGHING SONG - Round

Traditional

60 STAR SEARCH

Wolfgang Amadeus Mozart (1756 - 1791)

▶ Draw in the missing notes for "Twinkle, Twinkle, Little Star" before you play.

60 STAR SEARCH - For French Horns Only

▶ Draw in the missing notes for "Twinkle, Twinkle, Little Star" before you play.

61 GO FOR EXCELLENCE!

61 GO FOR EXCELLENCE! - For French Horns Only

 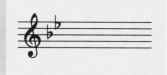

KEY SIGNATURE — This key signature means play all B's as B flats and all E's as E flats.

65 **THERE'S THE SAME MUSIC IN THE AIR** — George F. Root (1820 - 1895)

▶ Circle the notes changed by the key signature.

66 **SCALE SKILL**

66 **SCALE SKILL - For French Horns Only**

67 **FOR FRENCH HORNS ONLY**

PW21HF

17

 **DOTTED HALF NOTE**

A dot after a note adds half the value of the note.

♩ + • = ♩ + ♩ = ♩.

2 + 1 = 2 + 1 = 3 counts

TIME SIGNATURE

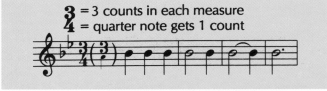

3 = 3 counts in each measure
4 = quarter note gets 1 count

DYNAMICS

forte (***f***) - loud
piano (***p***) - soft

68 WARM-UP

▶ Try playing this warm-up on your mouthpiece.

69 CHANNEL THREE

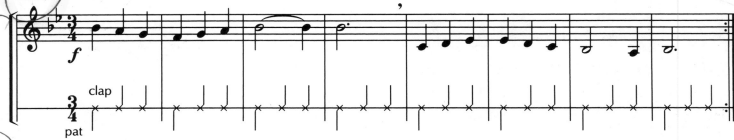

▶ Write in the counting for the top line before you play.

69 CHANNEL THREE - For French Horns Only

70 DOWN IN THE VALLEY

American Mountain Song

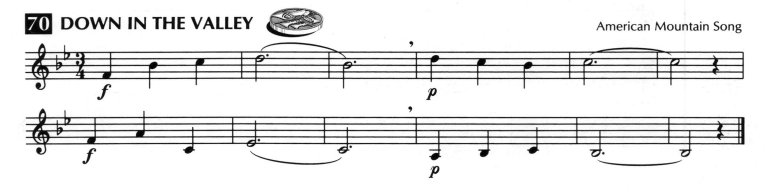

PW21HF

70 DOWN IN THE VALLEY - For French Horns Only

71 BROTHER MARTIN - Round

Latin American Folk Song

72 THE LITTLE FISH

Australian Folk Song

▶ Draw in a breath mark at the end of each phrase.

72 THE LITTLE FISH - For French Horns Only

▶ Draw in a breath mark at the end of each phrase.

73 GO FOR EXCELLENCE!

Czech Folk Song

"When Love Is Kind"

73 GO FOR EXCELLENCE! - For French Horns Only

"When Love Is Kind"

18

NATURAL

A natural sign cancels a flat or a sharp.
It remains in effect for the entire measure.

74 WARM-UP

▶ Try playing this warm-up on your mouthpiece.

75 OLD BLUE

Traditional

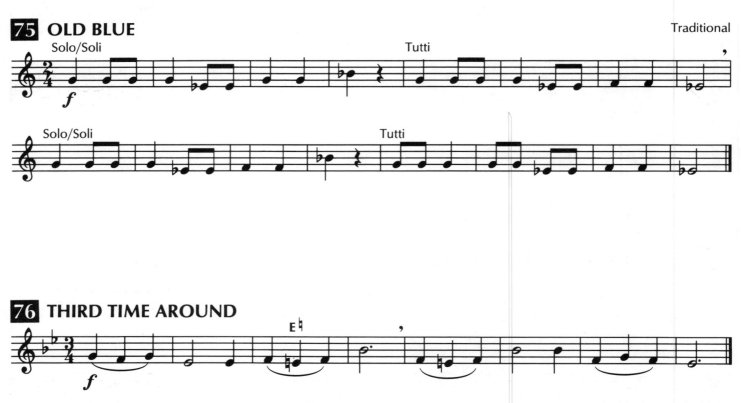

76 THIRD TIME AROUND

▶ Circle the notes changed by the key signature.

77 LULLABY - Duet Page 40 ▶

Traditional

78 MINUTEMAN MARCH

Robert Frost (b. 1942)

also played E♮ ↑

79 FOR FRENCH HORNS ONLY

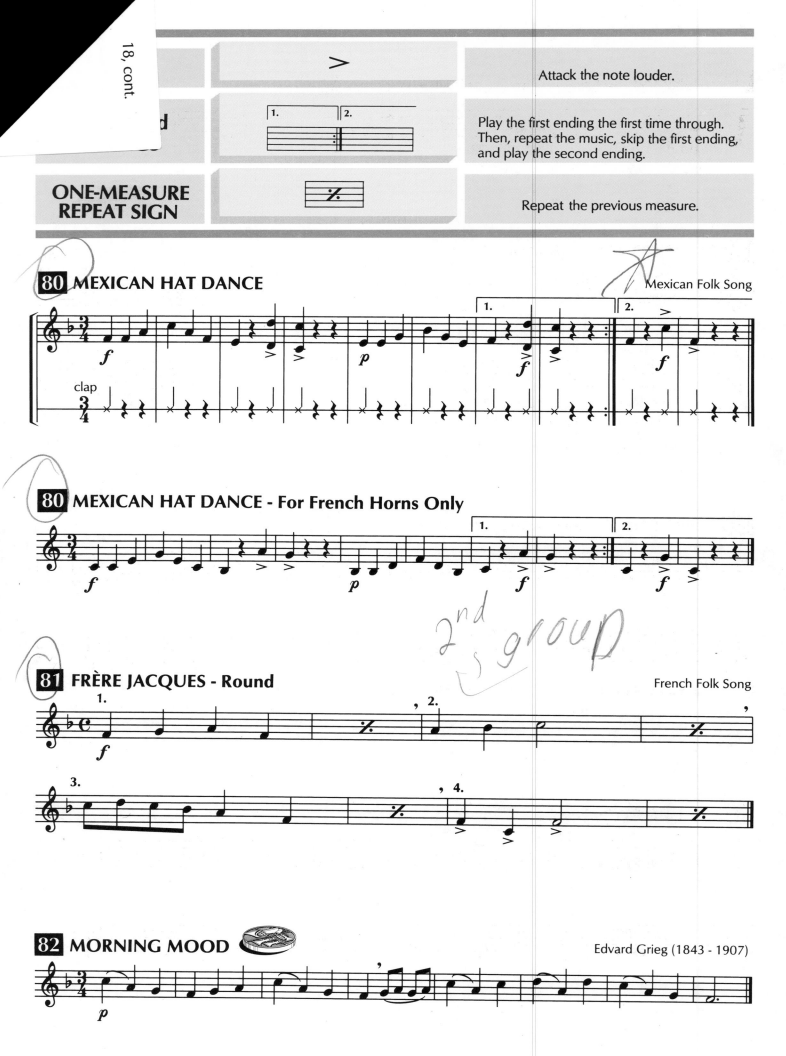

18, cont.	>	Attack the note louder.
	1. │ 2.	Play the first ending the first time through. Then, repeat the music, skip the first ending, and play the second ending.
ONE-MEASURE REPEAT SIGN	./.	Repeat the previous measure.

80 MEXICAN HAT DANCE

Mexican Folk Song

80 MEXICAN HAT DANCE - For French Horns Only

81 FRÈRE JACQUES - Round

French Folk Song

82 MORNING MOOD

Edvard Grieg (1843 - 1907)

82 MORNING MOOD - For French Horns Only

83 MING COURT Page 40 ▶▶▶

Chinese Folk Song

▶ Write an S under each slur and a T under the tie before you play.

83 MING COURT - For French Horns Only Page 40 ▶▶▶

▶ Write an S under each slur and a T under the tie before you play.

84 GO FOR EXCELLENCE!

The written piano accompaniment for SAWMILL CREEK is included on track 1 of CD 2 for easy access in a performance situation.

SAWMILL CREEK
Solo with Piano Accompaniment

Bruce Pearson (b. 1942)

▶ Go back to the first repeat sign.

LONG REST — Rest the number of measures indicated.

MONTEGO BAY
Band Arrangement

Calypso Song
arr. Chuck Elledge (b. 1961)

REGAL MARCH
Band Arrangement

Bruce Pearson (b. 1942)
arr. Chuck Elledge (b. 1961)

22

DIVISI	Part of the section plays the top notes and part of the section plays the bottom notes.	
UNISON	Everyone plays the same notes.	

85 WARM-UP

86 FULL OF HOT AIR

87 DANZA GIOVANNI

Italian Folk Song

88 F MAJOR SCALE SKILL (Concert B♭ Major)

88 C MAJOR SCALE SKILL - For French Horns Only

Arpeggio

Chords
div.

89 THE MAN ON THE FLYING TRAPEZE

George Leybourne (1842-1884)

▶ Go back to the first repeat sign.

89 THE MAN ON THE FLYING TRAPEZE - For French Horns Only

90 _____ Composer _____

your name

▶ Using the given rhythms, draw in notes to complete the melody. Title and play your composition.

91 FOR FRENCH HORNS ONLY

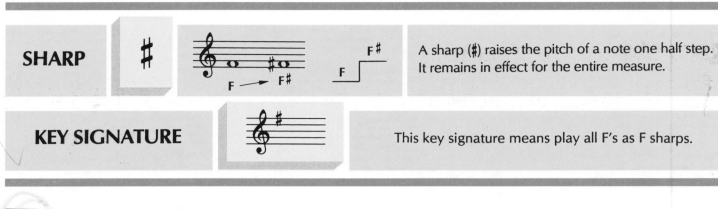

SHARP ♯

A sharp (♯) raises the pitch of a note one half step. It remains in effect for the entire measure.

F → F♯

KEY SIGNATURE

This key signature means play all F's as F sharps.

92 LOOK SHARP

f

92 LOOK SHARP - For French Horns Only

F sharp (F♯)

2
(1 2)

F♯

f

also played F♯

93 AURA LEE

G. R. Poulton (d. 1867)

p

93 AURA LEE - For French Horns Only

p

▶ Circle the notes changed by the key signature.

94 BARCAROLLE

Jacques Offenbach (1819 - 1880)

1.

2.

p

94 **BARCAROLLE - For French Horns Only**

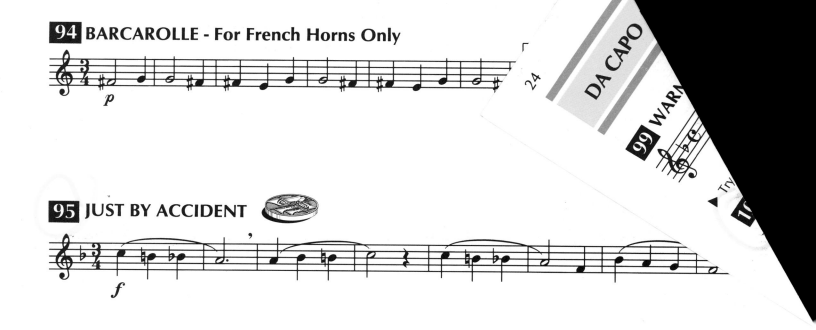

95 **JUST BY ACCIDENT**

96 **C MAJOR SCALE SKILL (Concert F Major)**

Arpeggio

Chords
div.

97 **SAILOR'S SONG** Page 40 Page 40

Solo/Soli

Tutti

1. 2.

98 **GO FOR EXCELLENCE!**

American Folk Song

"This Old Man"

...M-UP

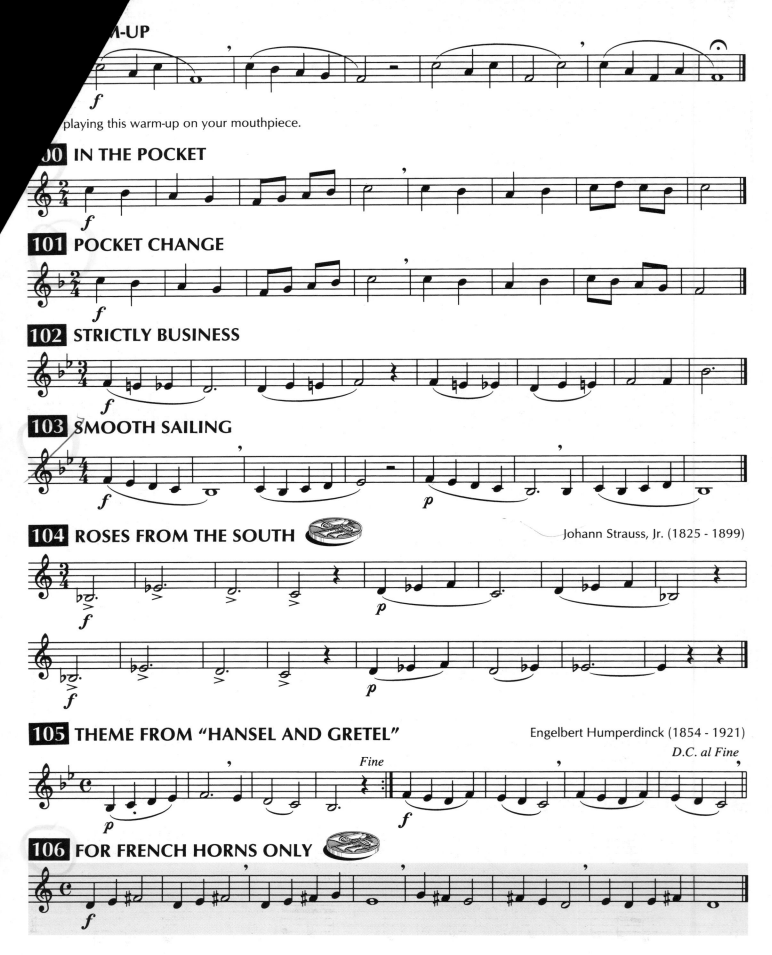

...playing this warm-up on your mouthpiece.

100 IN THE POCKET

101 POCKET CHANGE

102 STRICTLY BUSINESS

103 SMOOTH SAILING

104 ROSES FROM THE SOUTH

Johann Strauss, Jr. (1825 - 1899)

105 THEME FROM "HANSEL AND GRETEL"

Engelbert Humperdinck (1854 - 1921)

D.C. al Fine

106 FOR FRENCH HORNS ONLY

PW21HF

107 THAT'S A WRAP

108 POLLY WOLLY DOODLE Page 40 ▶

American Folk Song

clap

foot stomp

1.

2.

109 VOLGA BOAT SONG Page 40 ▶

Russian Folk Song

110 _____

Composer _____

your name

Hand Clappers

Knee Slappers

▶ Compose a duet (accompaniment) part for Knee Slappers. The first measure has been completed for you. Title and perform your composition.

111 GO FOR EXCELLENCE!

Tielman Susato (1500? - 1561?)

"Ronde"

SINGLE EIGHTH NOTE		A single eighth note is half as long as a quarter note. ♪ = ½ count
DOTTED QUARTER NOTE		A dot after a note adds half the value of the note. ♩ + . = ♩ + ♪ = ♩. 1 + ½ = 1 + ½ = 1 ½ counts

112 WARM-UP - Band Arrangement

▶ Try playing this warm-up on your mouthpiece.

113 SHORT CUT

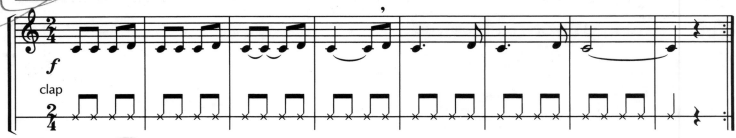

▶ Write in the counting for the top line before you play.

114 SPOT THE DOTS

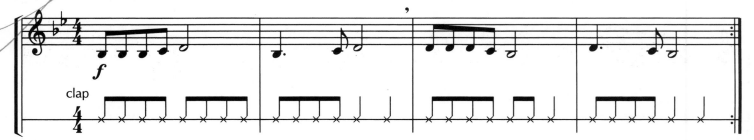

▶ Feel the pulse of three eighth notes during each dotted quarter note.

115 ALL THROUGH THE NIGHT

Welsh Folk Song

115 ALL THROUGH THE NIGHT - For French Horns Only

116 ALOUETTE

French–Canadian Folk Song

116 ALOUETTE - For French Horns Only

117 FOR FRENCH HORNS ONLY

118 JUST A LITTLE OFF THE TOP

119 TOP DRAWER - Duet

120 HOME ON THE RANGE

Page 41

Daniel E. Kelley (1843 - 1905)

▶ Circle the notes changed by the key signature.

120 **HOME ON THE RANGE - For French Horns Only** Page 41

▶ Circle the notes changed by the key signature.

121 **THE CONQUERING HERO - Duet**

George Frideric Handel (1685 - 1759)

122 **GO FOR EXCELLENCE!**

28

| TEMPOS | **Andante** - moderately slow
Moderato - moderate speed
Allegro - quick and lively | DYNAMICS | *mezzo forte* (***mf***) - medium loud |

123 WARM-UP - Band Arrangement

▶ Try playing this warm-up on your mouthpiece.

124 HIGH WINDS AHEAD

125 LOOK BEFORE YOU LEAP

126 B♭ MAJOR SCALE SKILL (Concert E♭ Major)

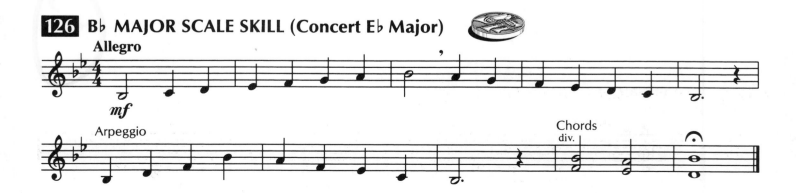

PW21HF

DYNAMICS	*mezzo piano* (**mp**) - medium soft

127 **VARIATIONS ON A THEME BY MOZART** Wolfgang Amadeus Mozart (1756 – 1791)

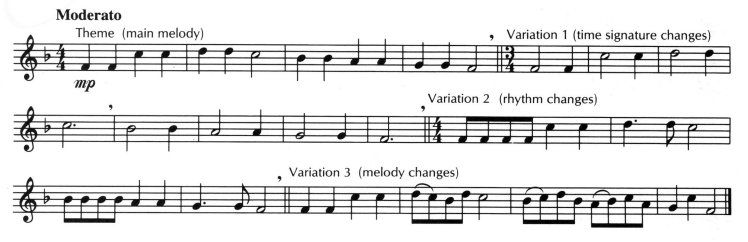

127 **VARIATIONS ON A THEME BY MOZART - For French Horns Only**

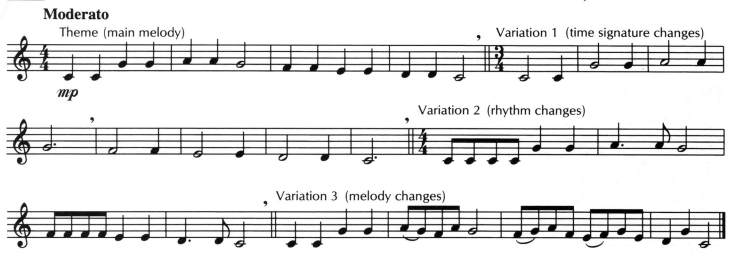

128 **FOR FRENCH HORNS ONLY**

DYNAMICS

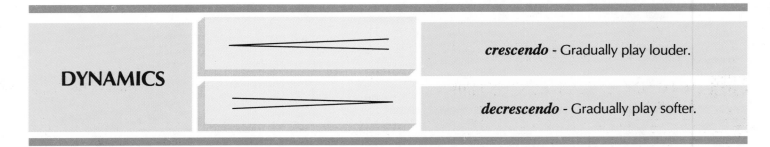

crescendo - Gradually play louder.

decrescendo - Gradually play softer.

129 SLIPPERY SLURS

Andante

130 WALTZ STREET

Moderato

131 THEME FROM "SYMPHONY NO. 9"

Ludwig van Beethoven (1770 - 1827)

Moderato

132 READY OR NOT

Andante

133 **ACH! DU LIEBER AUGUSTINE**

German Folk Song

Allegro

133 **ACH! DU LIEBER AUGUSTINE - For French Horns Only**

Allegro

134 **GO FOR EXCELLENCE!**

Page 41

Moderato

▶ Play using each of the following articulations: A. ♪♫♪   B. ♫♪♪   C. ♪♫♪

BALANCE BUILDER

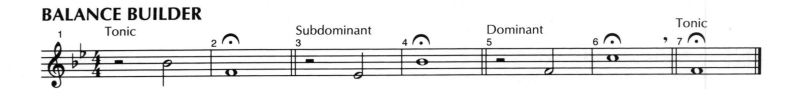

TRUMPET VOLUNTARY
Band Arrangement

Jeremiah Clarke (1674? - 1707)
arr. Bruce Pearson (b. 1942)

TEMPO

Ritardando (ritard. or rit.) - Gradually slow the tempo.

135 SAKURA - Duet

Japanese Folk Song

▶ Draw in a breath mark at the end of each phrase.

136 GRANDFATHER'S WHISKERS

American Folk Song

136 GRANDFATHER'S WHISKERS - For French Horns Only

137 TWINKLE VARIATION

Wolfgang Amadeus Mozart (1756 – 1791)

Composer _____ your name

▶ Compose a variation on "Twinkle, Twinkle, Little Star."

138 PARTNER SONGS - Duet

American Spirituals

138 PARTNER SONGS - Duet - For French Horns Only

139 **MANHATTAN BEACH MARCH**

John Philip Sousa (1854 - 1932)

140 **DYNAMIC DECISION**

Write in the following dynamics from softest to loudest: *mezzo forte   piano   forte   mezzo piano*

_____   _____   _____   _____

softest ←——————————————————————————————→ **loudest**

141 **FOR FRENCH HORNS ONLY**

TEMPO	Largo - slow

142 **"LARGO" FROM THE NEW WORLD SYMPHONY** Antonin Dvořák (1841 - 1904)

143 **JUST FINE** Page 41 ▶

144 **CHORALE - Duet** Lowell Mason (1792 - 1872)

144 **CHORALE - Duet - For French Horns Only**

Largo

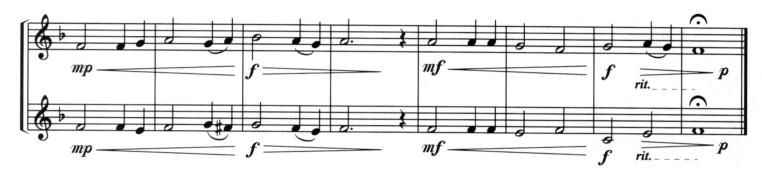

145 **TEMPO TIME**

Write in the following tempos from slowest to fastest: **Andante   Allegro   Moderato   Largo**

_____   _____   _____   _____

slowest ⟵   ⟶ fastest

146 **GO FOR EXCELLENCE!**

Allegro

34

147 RICOCHET ROCK

Chuck Elledge (b. 1961)

147 RICOCHET ROCK - For French Horns Only

148 LOCH LOMOND

Scottish Folk Song

148 LOCH LOMOND - For French Horns Only

149 SHALOM, CHAVERIM

Hebrew Folk Song

▶ Draw in a breath mark at the end of each phrase.

149 SHALOM, CHAVERIM - For French Horns Only

▶ Draw in a breath mark at the end of each phrase.

150 _____ Composer _____

your name

▶ Compose an ending for this melody. Title and play your composition.

151 FOR FRENCH HORNS ONLY

35

152 GRANDFATHER'S CLOCK   Page 41 ▶   Henry C. Work (1832 - 1884)

152 GRANDFATHER'S CLOCK - For French Horns Only   Page 41 ▶

▶ Circle the notes changed by the key signature.

153 KUM BA YAH   African Folk Song

153 KUM BA YAH - For French Horns Only

PW21HF

154 **GRANT US PEACE - Round**

German Canon

Andante

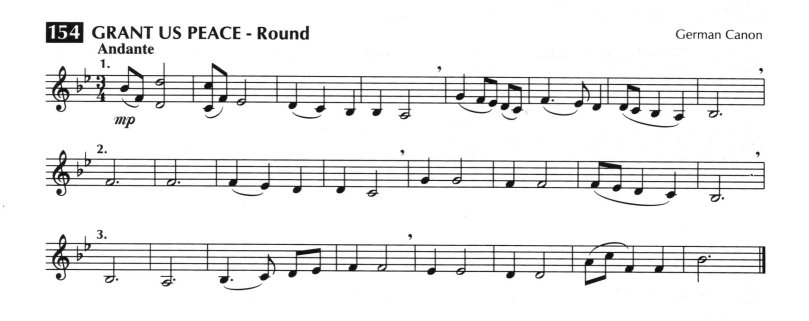

154 **GRANT US PEACE - Round - For French Horns Only**

Andante

155 **GO FOR EXCELLENCE!**

Moderato

EMPEROR'S HYMN
from the "Emperor" String Quartet Op. 76, no. 3
Solo with Piano Accompaniment

Franz Joseph Haydn
(1732 – 1809)

ROCKIN' RONDEAU
Band Arrangement

Based on a theme by
Jean-Joseph Mouret (1682 – 1738)
arr. Chuck Elledge (b. 1961)

⏩ EXCELLERATORS - FOR FRENCH HORNS ONLY

TIE

A tie is a curved line that connects two notes of the <u>same</u> pitch. Tied notes are played as one unbroken note.

SLUR

A slur is a curved line that connects two or more notes of <u>different</u> pitches. Tongue only the first note of a slur.

4A

4B

12A

12B

23A

23B

39

58

➡ EXCELLERATORS - FOR FRENCH HORNS ONLY

▶EXCELLERATORS - FOR FRENCH HORNS ONLY

SCALE STUDIES

F MAJOR SCALE (Concert B♭ Major)

Arpeggio

Thirds

B♭ MAJOR SCALE (Concert E♭ Major)

Arpeggio

Thirds

C MAJOR SCALE (Concert F Major)

Arpeggio

Thirds

E♭ MAJOR SCALE (Concert A♭ Major)

Arpeggio

Thirds

CHROMATIC SCALE

RHYTHM STUDIES

$\frac{4}{4}$ or **C**

RHYTHM STUDIES

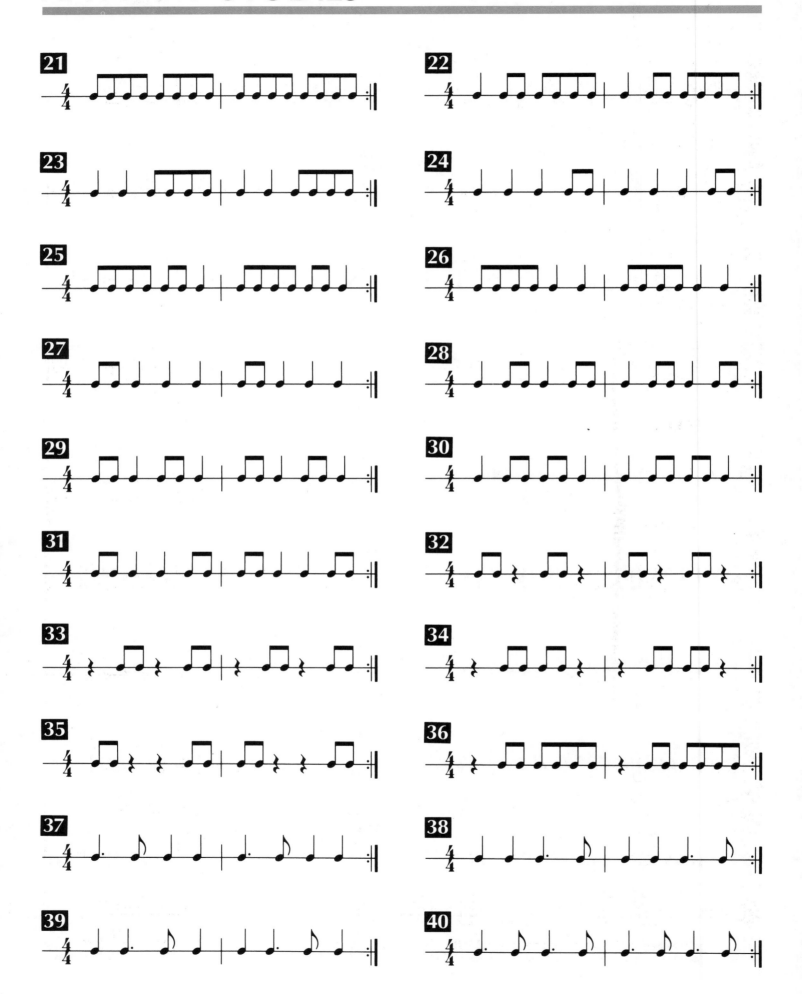

RHYTHM STUDIES

GLOSSARY/INDEX

STANDARD OF EXCELLENCE

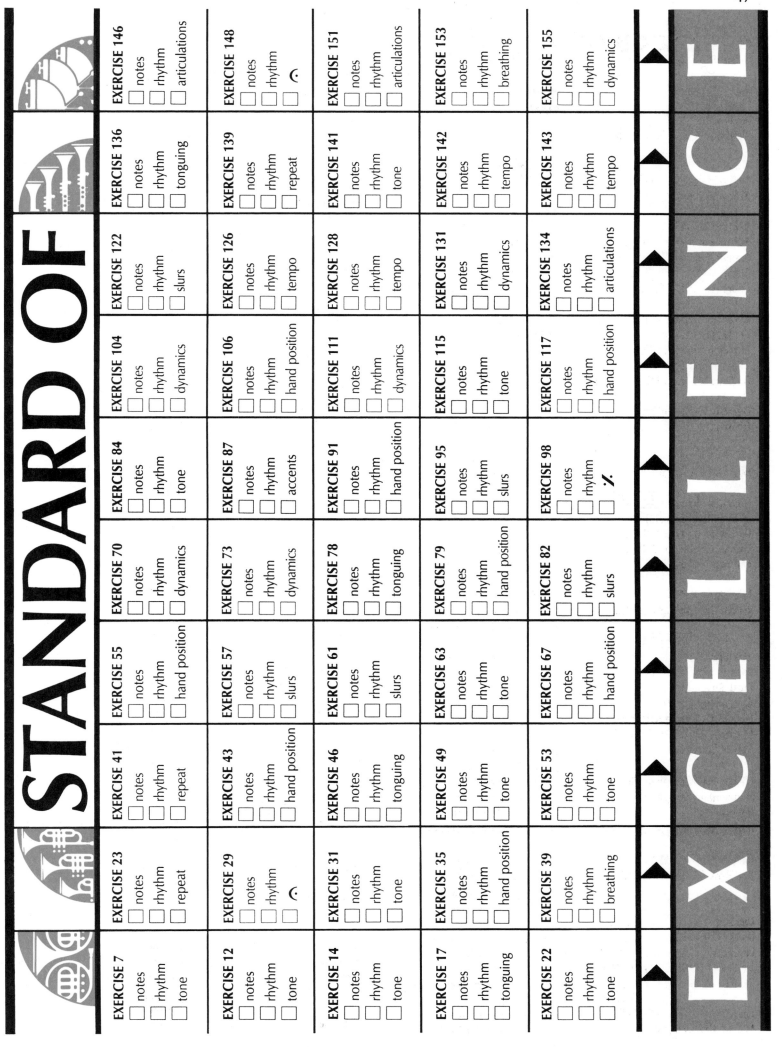

EXERCISE 7 — ☐ notes ☐ rhythm ☐ tone

EXERCISE 12 — ☐ notes ☐ rhythm ☐ tone

EXERCISE 14 — ☐ notes ☐ rhythm ☐ tone

EXERCISE 17 — ☐ notes ☐ rhythm ☐ tonguing

EXERCISE 22 — ☐ notes ☐ rhythm ☐ tone

EXERCISE 23 — ☐ notes ☐ rhythm ☐ repeat

EXERCISE 29 — ☐ notes ☐ rhythm ☐ 𝄐

EXERCISE 31 — ☐ notes ☐ rhythm ☐ tone

EXERCISE 35 — ☐ notes ☐ rhythm ☐ hand position

EXERCISE 39 — ☐ notes ☐ rhythm ☐ breathing

EXERCISE 41 — ☐ notes ☐ rhythm ☐ repeat

EXERCISE 43 — ☐ notes ☐ rhythm ☐ hand position

EXERCISE 46 — ☐ notes ☐ rhythm ☐ tonguing

EXERCISE 49 — ☐ notes ☐ rhythm ☐ tone

EXERCISE 53 — ☐ notes ☐ rhythm ☐ tone

EXERCISE 55 — ☐ notes ☐ rhythm ☐ hand position

EXERCISE 57 — ☐ notes ☐ rhythm ☐ slurs

EXERCISE 61 — ☐ notes ☐ rhythm ☐ slurs

EXERCISE 63 — ☐ notes ☐ rhythm ☐ tone

EXERCISE 67 — ☐ notes ☐ rhythm ☐ hand position

EXERCISE 70 — ☐ notes ☐ rhythm ☐ dynamics

EXERCISE 73 — ☐ notes ☐ rhythm ☐ dynamics

EXERCISE 78 — ☐ notes ☐ rhythm ☐ tonguing

EXERCISE 79 — ☐ notes ☐ rhythm ☐ hand position

EXERCISE 82 — ☐ notes ☐ rhythm ☐ slurs

EXERCISE 84 — ☐ notes ☐ rhythm ☐ tone

EXERCISE 87 — ☐ notes ☐ rhythm ☐ accents

EXERCISE 91 — ☐ notes ☐ rhythm ☐ hand position

EXERCISE 95 — ☐ notes ☐ rhythm ☐ slurs

EXERCISE 98 — ☐ notes ☐ rhythm ☐ ⁒

EXERCISE 104 — ☐ notes ☐ rhythm ☐ dynamics

EXERCISE 106 — ☐ notes ☐ rhythm ☐ hand position

EXERCISE 111 — ☐ notes ☐ rhythm ☐ dynamics

EXERCISE 115 — ☐ notes ☐ rhythm ☐ tone

EXERCISE 117 — ☐ notes ☐ rhythm ☐ hand position

EXERCISE 122 — ☐ notes ☐ rhythm ☐ slurs

EXERCISE 126 — ☐ notes ☐ rhythm ☐ tempo

EXERCISE 128 — ☐ notes ☐ rhythm ☐ tempo

EXERCISE 131 — ☐ notes ☐ rhythm ☐ dynamics

EXERCISE 134 — ☐ notes ☐ rhythm ☐ articulations

EXERCISE 136 — ☐ notes ☐ rhythm ☐ tonguing

EXERCISE 139 — ☐ notes ☐ rhythm ☐ repeat

EXERCISE 141 — ☐ notes ☐ rhythm ☐ tone

EXERCISE 142 — ☐ notes ☐ rhythm ☐ tempo

EXERCISE 143 — ☐ notes ☐ rhythm ☐ tempo

EXERCISE 146 — ☐ notes ☐ rhythm ☐ articulations

EXERCISE 148 — ☐ notes ☐ rhythm ☐ 𝄐

EXERCISE 151 — ☐ notes ☐ rhythm ☐ articulations

EXERCISE 153 — ☐ notes ☐ rhythm ☐ breathing

EXERCISE 155 — ☐ notes ☐ rhythm ☐ dynamics

EXCELLENCE

THE FRENCH HORN

FRENCH HORN HISTORY

The horn comes from a long tradition of instruments first used in ancient China (2000 B.C.), Egypt (1500 B.C.), and Scandinavia (1000 B.C.). These instruments were used for signaling and ceremony. However, because they had no valves, only a few notes could be played. By Roman times, and for centuries thereafter, valveless "natural" horns were common at military and civilian events.

In the 1600's the natural horn was used in the royal mounted hunt. The instrument was coiled and fit over the arm of the player who rode with the hunt, playing fanfares and horn calls.

The horn became a regular member of the orchestra during the 1700's. Early in the century, a horn pitched in F was made in Vienna. This instrument had five detachable pieces of tubing called crooks. Crooks lengthened or shortened the horn so it could be played in the best key for the music. By employing crooks and using the right hand in the bell to stop certain notes, a skilled musician could play any note of the scale.

The invention of valves in 1815 made the awkward crooks obsolete. Two types of valves were developed: rotary (revolving cylinder) valves, and piston (up and down) valves. The French made smaller bored horns with piston valves, while the Germans created larger bored horns with rotary valves. It is the German version that is referred to in America as a French horn.

In 1898, a German named Fritz Kruspe introduced the double horn. The double horn combines the single F and single B♭ horns into one instrument. It is widely accepted and played by virtually all professional players today.

French horns are typically made of brass or other metal, usually silver-plated or lacquered. Besides orchestras, they are played in bands, woodwind quintets, and brass ensembles.

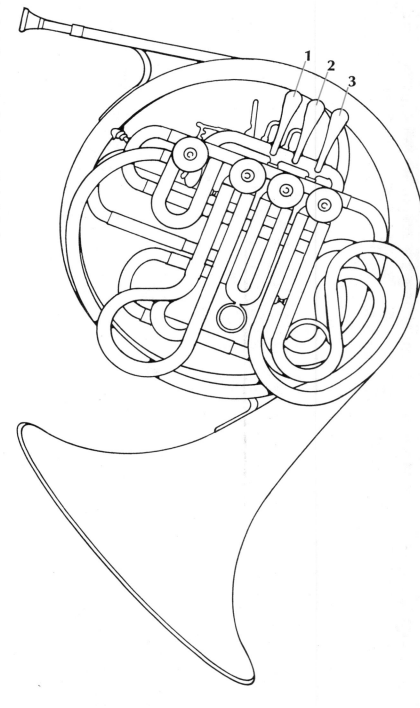

FRENCH HORN SURVIVAL KIT

- ☐ soft, clean cloth
- ☐ valve oil
- ☐ mute
- ☐ pencil
- ☐ band music
- ☐ mouthpiece cleaning brush
- ☐ slide grease
- ☐ extra string for valves
- ☐ method book
- ☐ music stand